3

But hang on!

Ram is big.
How can he get
on to the top
of the hut?

How can Ram
join the gang?

The Top of the Hut Gang

Written by
Cath Jones

Illustrated by
Andy Hamilton

This is the Top of the Hut gang: Owl, Wombat and Possum.

Ram is not in the gang.

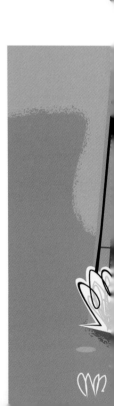

Down in the hut Ram is sad.

How can Ram join
Owl, Wombat and Possum?

7

Ram got a cannon!

Then Ram got a helmet.

The top of the hut
is the target!

Will Ram get to the top?

9

Bang! Pow!

Then, **Thud!**

Ram hit Owl!

Wombat fell off the top of the hut!

Possum got the hick-ups!

Possum fell off the hut as well!

That is how Ram got into
the top of the hut gang!